OXFORD*Playscripts*

●●●●●●●●●●●●●●●●●●●●●●●●●●●●●●●●●●●●●

Series Editor – Bill Lucas

Mary Shelley   *adapted by Philip Pullman*

Frankenstein

Oxford University Press

Oxford University Press, Walton Street, Oxford OX2 6DP

Oxford New York Toronto
Delhi Bombay Calcutta Madras Karachi
Kuala Lumpur Singapore Hong Kong Tokyo
Nairobi Dar es Salaam Cape Town
Melbourne Auckland Madrid

and associate companies in
Berlin Ibadan

Oxford is a trade mark of Oxford University Press

This collection © Oxford University Press 1990
This adaptation of *Frankenstein* © Philip Pullman 1990
Activities © Bill Lucas 1990
Reprinted 1991 (twice), 1992, 1993

ISBN 0 19 831267 9

Typeset by Pentacor PLC, High Wycombe, Bucks

Printed and bound by Butler & Tanner Ltd,
Frome and London

Contents

Characters

Captain Walton	*An Arctic explorer – tough, bearded, wearing furs. A man who has been in many dangerous places and survived, but who has come across something now that has shaken him to the depths.*
Frankenstein	*Young and idealistic – a dreamer, full of strange ideas, who believes that his work will improve the world.*
Clerval	*The same age as Frankenstein. Realistic and humorous, he is impressed by his friend's achievements but anxious about their effects.*
Landlady	*Middle-aged, probably, but it doesn't matter.*
Elizabeth	*A year or two younger than Frankenstein. She is devoted to his father and to William, and she loves Frankenstein without understanding him.*
The Monster	*It is important that he should look hideous. He is made of corpses, after all. But in the novel he is shown as being very strong and agile, and although when he first comes to life he cannot move easily, it makes him much more impressive in the later Acts if he is graceful and powerful and does not lurch about clumsily. His voice should be impressive.*
Felix	*Young, quick-tempered, fiery. He and Agathe are political refugees.*
Agathe	*Although she is blind, she should move about the room as easily as a sighted person. She knows it well, knows where everything is. It is when she first becomes aware that something is wrong that she begins to look vulnerable.*
Ghost of Willliam	*This is best played in a dead white mask, to give the effect of something or someone not quite alive.*
The Monster's Bride	*She should be as hideous as he is. When he first sees her, he is shocked.*
Servant	*Male*

Prologue
....

The Arctic. A landscape of bright snow and ice.

*Enter **Captain Walton**, clothed in furs.*

He speaks quietly, thoughtfully, as if recollecting a deep experience.

Captain Walton Some time ago, I had the command of a ship on an expedition to the Arctic Circle. We sailed further north than anyone had ever gone before, and then there came a day when we could go no further because the ice had closed us in. Weeks went by; months passed, and still we couldn't move. Strange things happen to your mind in the regions of eternal snow. The sailors began to report seeing things, impossible things, and hearing voices in the empty air – one voice like someone crying in pain or anguish, another voice that was deep and harsh and monstrous, howling of revenge. I began to worry that they'd go mad with fear, crazy with isolation; I began to suspect that there were ghosts in the air, evil spirits behind the bright light glaring on the snow . . . And then I saw it myself, and I could doubt no longer. In the distance, a sledge was moving across the ice, pulled by a team of dogs, and driving it was a creature like a man but huge and hideous beyond belief. And pursuing it – always in pursuit but never catching up – was a man on foot. We watched from the deck, the sailors and I, and then the man fell down and lay still on the snow. I sent out a party to bring him in. He told us that his name was . . . Frankenstein. We laid him in my cabin and looked after him, and presently he'd recovered enough to tell us his story. And a strange one it was . . .

He exits quietly.

*As he goes off, the light fades and the curtain rises to show **Frankenstein**'s room in Ingolstadt for Act One.*

Act One
············

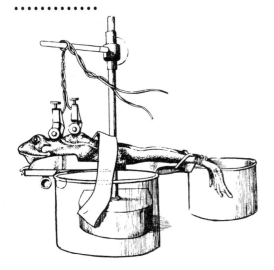

Frankenstein

Frankenstein's room. It has high, arched windows through which can be seen mountains and forest. At the moment moonlight is shining through. The light is dim and flickers as clouds pass in front of the moon. Sinister music plays.

*Then a hand reaches down from above, as if from the roof, and pulls the window open from the outside. A second later the shape of a man – **Frankenstein** – is seen to climb athletically down the outside and in through the window. He brings with him a wire which seems to be attached to something up on the roof. Because of the dim light in the room it is impossible to be certain what he is doing.*

He leans out of the window and calls up softly:

Clerval! Are you staying up there all night?

There is a scrambling sound from outside, as if the other person is not sure of his footing.

Clerval   *(From outside)*   I can't find the right place – ah, here it is – where the devil do I put my foot?

*A leg can be seen waving uncertainly about, feeling for a foothold. **Frankenstein** takes it and guides it to safety. A moment later, **Clerval** appears in the window and jumps down to join **Frankenstein**. They are both in their early twenties: **Frankenstein** intense, poetic; **Clerval** stout, cheerful, matter-of-fact. **Frankenstein** lights a lamp. The room is an odd mixture of shabby sitting-room and cluttered laboratory. Phials and bottles of chemicals and preserved specimens of various kinds line the shelves. A large, electrical-looking machine stands in the corner. On a bench at the back lies something – obviously the **Monster** – covered by a sheet.*
*
Clerval rubs his hands with the cold and looks around curiously.*

Clerval	So this is where you lurk, Frankenstein! D'you know, the other students are convinced you're a wizard?
Frankenstein	A wizard! Why's that?

*Both men have heavy coats on. **Clerval** is carrying a rucksack, which he takes off and drops on the floor. **Frankenstein** reacts with nervous anger.*

Frankenstein	Don't drop that!
Clerval	I'm sorry. What's in it? It feels like several pounds of meat.
Frankenstein	Well, it's . . . just that. Several pounds of meat.
Clerval	I hope it tastes good. Where are you going to cook it? Don't you have a fire in here? It feels as cold as it does outside. Colder, if anything.

Frankenstein is busy adjusting the wire he has brought in, securing it to brackets around the walls, leading it to the bench.

Frankenstein	No. No fire. I keep it cold on purpose – it's the only way to preserve my specimens . . . I don't notice it any more. Hold this, would you . . .

*Gives the end of the wire to **Clerval**, then goes back and props the window open.*

Clerval	You're not going to leave it open? We'll freeze to death, man!
Frankenstein	You'll get used to it. The only problem comes when you have to do delicate work with your hands . . . There. That should fix it.

He stands back, surveying the arrangement of the wire.

Clerval	Remarkable. Extraordinary. A phenomenon. I congratulate you, Frankenstein. Now what the devil's it all about? You bring me clambering over the rooftops carrying your next week's suppers in a rucksack; suppers which, by the way, you intend to eat raw, since you don't go in for lighting fires; you fix a length of copper wire to the highest point of the house, and trail it all the way down here and leave me holding the end of it – what's it all about, Frankenstein?
Frankenstein	My dear fellow! Let me take it from you –

> *Takes the end of the wire and fastens it to a complicated piece of apparatus near the bench.*

There. Now you won't explode.

> ***Clerval** steps away hastily.*

Clerval	Explode?
Frankenstein	A joke. *(Solemnly)* Ha ha ha.
Clerval	Oh, a joke! I see. Ha ha.
Frankenstein	Sit down, Clerval, there's a good man. If you really want a fire, I suppose lighting one just this once won't make any difference. And to tell the truth, I feel like celebrating. D'you think there's going to be a storm?
Clerval	A storm? Oh, bound to be.

> *He sits in an armchair, then sits upright quickly and feels behind him. He brings out a human thigh-bone from behind the cushion and stares at it with distaste.*

Last night's supper? Or this morning's breakfast?

Frankenstein	So that's where it got to . . .

> *He takes it, puts it on a shelf, brings down a bottle of wine from which he pulls the cork by hand.*

Frankenstein	There's a glass on the floor beside the chair, Clerval. I've only got the one. We'll share it.

Clerval finds it. It's dirty and covered in dust.
Frankenstein rubs it on his sleeve before
pouring the wine in.

Frankenstein	Your good health!

Drinks deeply, fills the glass again, walks
*upstage, leaving **Clerval** waiting for his turn.*

Yes, if we're lucky tonight and it storms, and if my wire does the job it's supposed to, and if . . . well, my dear fellow, we're on the threshold of a new age.

Clerval	You don't say?
Frankenstein	There's no harm in telling you. It's bound to come out sooner or later, and you're an intelligent man, you'll understand . . .
Clerval	Kind of you. The wine, Frankenstein . . .
Frankenstein	Ah! Forgive me.

*Pours another glass, takes it to **Clerval**.*

Yes – my work. So they call me a wizard, do they? Perhaps they're not far wide of the mark. I expect two hundred years ago they'd have burnt me at the stake.

Clerval	Not a bad idea. Then we could have warmed ourselves up . . .

Rubs his hands, shivers . . .

Frankenstein	All right, all right. I'll light the fire.

He crosses to the grate. As he does so, there is a
distant rumble of thunder. He stops and looks
out, with an expression of satisfaction.

Hear that? It's away over the mountains just yet, but it's on its way
. . .

He stoops, strikes a flint and steel, and starts a fire in the grate. **Clerval** *huddles closer to it as* **Frankenstein** *goes to the window to peer out.*

Frankenstein   Another hour or so, I should think. You can see the lightning playing around the peaks.

Clerval   All right, let me guess. Storm – lightning – wire – electricity.

Frankenstein   Very good!

Clerval   Electricity . . . Umm. Magnetism? You've invented a way of making magnets?

Frankenstein   Nothing like it.

He comes to sit in the other chair, takes the wine glass and fills it again.

Frogs' legs.

Clerval   And the same to you. Or is that the menu?

Frankenstein   No! An Italian called Galvani – heard of him?

Clerval   I'm a philosopher, not a musician. All Italian composers sound the same to me.

Frankenstein   Nothing to do with music. He was a scientist, Clerval. A natural philosopher. He was dissecting a frog one day, and he found that the nerve in the leg responded to electricity. It twitched when a current passed through it.

Clerval Now I have heard about that, come to think of it. He thought there was a kind of animal electricity, didn't he? And is that what you're working on?

Frankenstein More or less. But there's no such thing as animal electricity – it's all one. The same force flows in your nerves as in the frog's, and the very same force flows through the lightning . . . did I ever tell you how I first realised what my life's work was to be? I was fourteen years old, at home at Geneva, on a night like this – a storm was threatening. They rise very quickly in the mountains there. Outside our front door, about twenty yards away, stood a great old oak tree. It had been there for three hundred years at least, and it was still green and strong. I'd climbed it, I'd sheltered under it, I'd carved my initials on the trunk . . . and just as the storm was at its height, I opened the door to look at the lightning. You've never seen such a storm! The tree was lit up bright, bright green by flash after flash, and the thunder was exploding around the house like artillery fire. Then without any warning the tree was engulfed in flame. A colossal blaze shot right out of it, all in a moment, and dazzled me so I could hardly see . . . when I opened my eyes again, only a moment later, the tree was gone. There was nothing there at all but a charred, smoking stump. That great living thing, smashed to atoms in an instant! And I thought: the power that can do that is the power of life and death. I'll harness it. I'll study it and master it and make it work for mankind.

Clerval I see. And now you've done it?

Frankenstein Nearly. Nearly, Clerval!

*Drains the glass, fills it again, hands it to **Clerval**.*

Clerval So . . . you're going to collect some electricity from the lightning, and bring it down here, and . . . what then?

Frankenstein And then . . . drink the wine.

***Clerval** raises his eyebrows, but drains the glass.*

Clerval	Well?
Frankenstein	And then this happens.

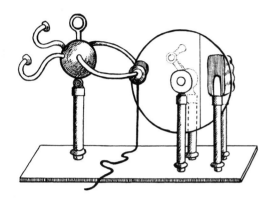

He gets up and goes to the bench. Next to it is a smaller trolley on wheels, on which is mounted a machine consisting of two glass discs that rotate in opposite directions when turned by a handle. Attached to a brass terminal is a twisted piece of wire that leads down to something on a slab of marble, covered at the moment with a cloth.
Clerval stands up to come closer and look at it.

Clerval   Now that I recognise . . . it's a what d'ye call it.

Frankenstein   This thing? It's a Wimshurst machine. And I expect you'll recognise this –

Takes the cloth away. **Clerval** *peers, then starts back in disgust.*

Clerval   It's a human hand!

A hand is lying flat on the slab, but we cannot see it clearly. That's what it is, however – yellowed, dried, and withered, and thoroughly revolting.

Where did you get that from?

Frankenstein   From the dissecting room at the University. Quite proper, I assure you. The chap it was attached to was hanged; he had no further use for it. As a matter of fact, he strangled his wife with it only last month.

Clerval   Good grief! Frankenstein, how can you joke about such things?

Frankenstein	Yes, of course, you're right. I'm sorry. It's the excitement, Clerval. I'm so close to . . . never mind. I'll show you what the machine does, if you're still interested.
Clerval	Of course I'm interested! But I don't care to be ghoulish about it.
Frankenstein	No, no. Heaven forbid.

He connects the wire to something on the bench, checks that all is ready, and takes the handle of the machine. Before he turns it:

Frankenstein	Think of this as . . . as a philosopher should, Clerval. There's no cause for shock or disgust in nature.
Clerval	I wonder. Carry on, then.

Frankenstein begins to turn the handle. The glass discs start rotating slowly in opposite directions; an electric hum fills the air; sparks are seen to jump from one brass terminal to another – all contributing to the impression of high powered electrical activity.

Frankenstein	There – can you see it? Can you see the finger twitching?
Clerval	(Leaning over, but not so as to obscure the audience's view) The index finger – yes! It's definitely moving – and now the thumb – Good God, Frankenstein, it's horrible!
Frankenstein	Philosophy, Clerval! Let me increase the charge . . .

Turns the handle faster. And suddenly the hand moves so that all the audience can see it: it curves up horribly, palm towards us, fingers curved and twitching. Clerval steps back and gasps.

Clerval	Ugghh!
Frankenstein	No – wait – that knob at the side of the bench –

He is still turning the handle vigorously, and he nods down in the direction he means.
Clerval comes closer, fascinated and horrified.

Clerval   This one?

Frankenstein   Turn it – slowly – when I tell you. Clockwise.

Clerval reaches for it.

Frankenstein   Now. *Slowly.*

Clerval turns it – and the hand slowly clenches.

Clerval   Good God!

He turns it back – the hand unclenches again, and stands up from the bench stiff and twitching as before.

Frankenstein   Again.

Clerval does it again.

Clerval   Extraordinary!

Frankenstein   That's not all. Let it open again – that's it – now try the lever next to the knob. Gently, gently. I haven't tried this yet.

Frankenstein is still turning the handle, the glass discs are still revolving, the sparks are still crackling. Clerval reaches for the lever and moves it a fraction, then a bit further – and the forefinger curls forward slowly to meet the thumb.
Clerval leans over, as excited as Frankenstein by what he can make the hand do. Like two small boys, they play with it for a moment or two –

Clerval	Look! It can bring its thumb across – let me just try the knob at the same time –
Frankenstein	That's it! Just a bit more –
Clerval	And . . . there! The thumb's touching the little finger! Wonderful!
Frankenstein	Excellent! Now we'll try the –

>   *A flash from the machine, a loud crack, and*
>   *they start back as the hand falls lifelessly to the*
>   *bench.*

Clerval	What happened?
Frankenstein	The charge. I was turning the handle too fast – it's burnt the wire out, look.

>   *He holds up a charred end of wire.* **Clerval**
>   *mops his brow.*

Clerval	Frankenstein, I'm astounded. This is the greatest discovery of the age! A wonderful piece of work!
Frankenstein	A step or two beyond Signor Galvani, eh?
Clerval	It's beyond anything I've ever heard of. When are you going to publish it? The world should be hearing about your genius, my friend! You should be honoured – you should have doctorates, professorships –

>   *Seizes the bottle and glass and pours some*
>   *wine.*

Clerval	To your fame, Frankenstein!

>   *Drinks deeply, then makes a face.*

And I hope you'll buy better wine when you're famous. That's if you want company when you drink it.

Frankenstein covers the hand again with the cloth and wheels the trolley back out of the way as he speaks.

Frankenstein   You're a good fellow, Clerval. That's why I wanted you to see what I'd done. You've no idea how lonely it's been . . . I've been working at this for six years now. Six years! I mastered the physiology of the hand a long time ago. I could do this demonstration in my first year of study . . .

*Clerval sits, and **Frankenstein** comes to join him.*

Clerval   You mean there's more?

Frankenstein   That was only the first crude attempt. I took that hand on purpose to show you; I could have shown you four years ago. I . . . as a matter of fact, I wasn't telling the truth when I said where it came from. I hope you won't mention it to anyone. I . . . well, I dug it up last night.

Clerval   You *what*?

Frankenstein   I've begged the University for specimens. They say I've had all their best material for years, and produced nothing to show for it. How could I show them that? Can you imagine the reaction? They won't give me anything now. I have to . . .

*He shrugs. **Clerval** is taken aback.*

Clerval   You dig them up? Good Lord, Frankenstein, how many corpses are there without hands in our graveyards?

Frankenstein   Not just hands. D'you think I want to do it this way? I'd far rather have the use of a proper dissecting-room, and all the resources of the University – I have to go without meals to buy the chemicals I need, I have nowhere to store my specimens, my landlady drives me mad with her incessant questions –

Clerval   What d'you mean, *not just hands*? What else –

A thought strikes him suddenly – he looks at the rucksack with horrified suspicion.

Clerval	What's in there?
Frankenstein	Oh, nothing – that's just –

> *He gets up anxiously, crosses to where the rucksack is lying – but before he can pick it up, there is a loud knock. He starts nervously.*

Landlady's voice	Herr Frankenstein! Are you there?
Frankenstein	*(To **Clerval**)* My landlady – *(Calling)* Yes, Frau Liebermann?
Landlady	A constable to see you. What's going on, Herr Frankenstein?
Frankenstein	I haven't the faintest idea, Frau Liebermann, probably some silly mistake. I'll come down and see him. *(To **Clerval**)* I'll be back in a minute. Be a good fellow – don't touch anything . . .

> *He leaves. **Clerval** sits for a moment, thoughtful; then gets up, crosses to the rucksack and picks it up, feeling its weight, feeling it through the canvas: then he turns it around, and sees a spreading bloodstain. He drops it with horror.*

Clerval	Good grief . . .

> *He backs away, then goes to the window and looks out.*

Frankenstein, are you mad, or am I? . . . there's going to be a storm soon, I can feel it.

> *He shivers.*

And then what? Lightning . . . lightning! Electricity! The hand . . . what on earth?

> *He follows the wire to its destination on the large bench with the sheeted body of the **Monster**. We can see him steeling himself to look.*

Clerval	Frankenstein, what have you done?

> *He reaches out to pull the sheet down, nervously – when there's a timid knock at the door.*
> *He starts guiltily.*

	Yes? Yes, who's that?
Elizabeth's voice	Victor? May I come in?
Clerval	It's not Victor – but yes, come in, come in ...

> *The door opens and **Elizabeth** comes in, dressed for a journey: bonnet, cloak, etc. She is young, about eighteen, and at the moment, nervous.*

Elizabeth	I beg your pardon, sir – the landlady said I would find Herr Frankenstein's rooms up here –
Clerval	Yes, that's right. This is his place. I'm a friend of his – Henri de Clerval. He's ... I thought he was downstairs at the moment? Seeing a visitor?
Elizabeth	The landlady was not very friendly. I ... I'm his cousin, monsieur. I've come a long way.

> *She sways as if tired or about to faint.*
> ***Clerval** helps her to a chair.*

Clerval	Mademoiselle ... please, sit down. I've sure your cousin won't be long.
Elizabeth	Thank you, monsieur, I'm tired; I've come a long way today. He wasn't expecting me, but there was no time to let him know I was coming ...
Clerval	Is there any trouble, mademoiselle? He's never mentioned his family. I thought he was alone in the world.

Elizabeth	His father's very ill. His mother is dead; there's only his father and me and his little brother, and when his father fell ill I wrote to Victor and told him, but he never answered my letters. I didn't know what else to do.
Clerval	He's wrapped up in his researches, I'm afraid. A brilliant man, but . . . well, you know him, after all. Wasn't he like this when he was a child?
Elizabeth	Yes, I suppose he was. Monsieur de Clerval, is he in trouble?
Clerval	Trouble? Why?
Elizabeth	Something's not right. I'm worried. I have such dreams . . . I see Victor in them, and there's something horrible pursuing him – or is he pursuing it? But there's such a sense of doom and despair . . . I'm sorry. I shouldn't be telling you this. Where is Victor now?
Clerval	Seeing a visitor. He won't be long.

Pause. She shivers.

Clerval	You're cold. Let me shut the window.

He crosses to the window. She has her back to him; he sees the wire again, follows it with his eyes to the sheeted figure, and hesitates.

Clerval	Mademoiselle . . . have you anywhere to stay? There's a comfortable inn just across the square. I'd be glad to take your luggage across there for you.
Elizabeth	That's kind of you, monsieur. You're right; I can hardly stay here, and Victor isn't expecting me. My valise is in the hall.
Clerval	I'll go and do it now. Your cousin will be up soon, I'm sure . . .

He goes out quickly. She sits still for a moment, looking weary and anxious.
In the distance there is a rumble of thunder. Startled, she looks around at the window, and sees that it is still open. She gets up to close it – and her eye is caught by the sheeted form on

	the bench. Hesitantly she approaches – reaches out to touch it – is about to pull back the sheet, when the door bursts open and –
Frankenstein	No! Don't touch it!
	He runs in and pulls her away, then peers out of the window and up into the sky.
Elizabeth	Victor! Whatever's the matter? What is it?
Frankenstein	Elizabeth – you mustn't stay here. Not now. Where's Clerval?
Elizabeth	He went to take my valise to the inn across the square – but Victor, what's going on? Are you in trouble?
Frankenstein	No, no – but I'm in the middle of a crucial experiment, I can't leave it – you haven't touched anything?
Elizabeth	Not a thing. But Victor – what's the matter with you? I've come all the way from home, I'm tired and cold, I haven't seen you for six months – you haven't even asked me why I'm here.
Frankenstein	I'm sorry . . . why *are* you here? Is something wrong?
Elizabeth	It's your father, Victor. He's very ill.
Frankenstein	Oh no . . . what is it? How long's he been unwell?
Elizabeth	It's an affliction of the lungs. I wrote to you a month ago, when it first came on, and again a fortnight later, and again last week. What are you doing, Victor? Why don't you answer my letters? You haven't even read them! If you want to see your father alive, you'd better come home tomorrow.
Frankenstein	Tomorrow! But –
Elizabeth	But what? What's more important than that? To him, I mean. I can see there's plenty more important to you. A son who doesn't come when his father's dying . . . oh, you make me ill. Now I'm going to the inn to find something to eat and go to bed. I'm very tired.

She moves towards the door. He tries to hold her back.

Frankenstein   No, Elizabeth, don't – you're right, I'll come back with you – but my work, you don't understand, it's reached the point I've been working towards for six years –

Elizabeth   Understand? How can I understand a son who cares nothing for his father? How can I understand someone who shuts himself up in a dirty dusty smelly freezing cold room like this, and says that *this* is more important to him than his family?

He tries to hold her still, but she shakes him off.

Elizabeth   No – don't try to hold me back. If this is what matters to you, Victor, then so be it. I've done my duty – now I'm going to lie down, because I'm tired, and in the morning I shall go back home, whether or not you come with me.

She goes out. He sinks into a chair, despairing.

Frankenstein   Must it finish, then? So close . . . so nearly ready!

He holds his head in his hands.
After a moment there comes a tremendous clap of thunder – deafening – as if right overhead. **Frankenstein** *sits up at once and stares at the form on the bench. It is quite still. He jumps up and runs to the window, through which we can hear the start of a heavy rainfall. He looks out and upwards, and is outlined in a flash of lightning. He looks round again, checking the wire, but still the figure lies unmoving. Then comes more thunder – longer and even louder than before.*
Feverishly he runs to the bench, checks the wire and folds back the sheet a little way so that he can see the **Monster's** *face.*

Frankenstein   It must be tonight – it must be!

A frantic knocking at the door.

Clerval	*(Outside)* Frankenstein! Open up! Open up!
Frankenstein	No! Go away, Clerval! I can't be disturbed!
Clerval	Frankenstein, I must talk to you –
Frankenstein	Impossible! Go away, man!

More furious hammering on the door.

Clerval	You must let me in – I know what you're doing, Frankenstein –

***Frankenstein** runs to the door.*

Frankenstein	Clerval, I beg you – leave me alone – you don't know how dangerous this could be –

*But the door bursts open. **Frankenstein** is flung aside as **Clerval** runs in, looks around, and runs to where the **Monster** is lying. He tears off the sheet and flings it to the floor as **Frankenstein** recovers and runs across to tear him away.*

Frankenstein	Don't! Don't touch it! The lightning could strike at any moment –

They struggle in front of the window, illuminated by another great flash of lightning; and almost at once comes the thunder. They freeze, both looking in apprehension at the bench.
*Then comes another flash, lighting up the whole room, accompanied by showers of sparks and wreaths of smoke – and on the bench, the **Monster** tenses convulsively.*

Clerval	No!
Frankenstein	Leave it – leave it –

*Another flash, more thunder – and this time, the **Monster** really comes alive, thrashing from side to side as if trying to sit up. **Clerval** breaks away from **Frankenstein** and stares at it in horror.*

Clerval   Frankenstein – what have you created?

Frankenstein   I told you not to come in!

Clerval   This is pure evil, Frankenstein –

*He starts forward as if to destroy it, but **Frankenstein**, seeing his intention, seizes a chair and strikes him with it from behind. The chair breaks – **Clerval** falls stunned.*

Frankenstein   Oh, my friend – you don't know how important it is –

*He runs to the **Monster**'s side and tears off the wires, and then helps it to sit up. The storm is still raging outside, and there are flashes of lightning. The **Monster** is enormously tall and powerfully built. His open eyes are hideous, red-rimmed and glaring in a waxy yellow face. His lips are black, scars criss-cross his cheeks, and his face is framed with matted black hair. He is naked to the waist. He wears nothing but simple breeches.*
*The **Monster** stands there, swaying as **Frankenstein** moves back to get a better look at his creation. Then the **Monster** raises a hand, and **Frankenstein** reaches up to touch it.*

Frankenstein   My creature! And living! Let me see you – let me look at you – ah . . .

*He runs his hands over the **Monster**'s limbs, checking their soundness, helping him balance upright. The **Monster**'s eyes follow him, as if confused.*
*Then **Frankenstein** stands back, and a first realisation of what he has made passes over him. He shudders.*

Frankenstein   But you're not what I thought you'd be . . . I thought I was making an angel! D'you know that? I thought I was making something better than human! Something so precious and beautiful that everyone would love it – and look at you. Look at what I've done.

*The **Monster** takes a lurching step towards him. **Frankenstein** backs away nervously.*

Frankenstein   No! This isn't what I wanted. Oh, dear God, what have I done? Is it alive after all?

*The **Monster** makes a strange noise.*

Frankenstein   No! I didn't mean this! I didn't want this at all –

He turns away, and with a cry of fear and horror, runs out of the room.

Frankenstein   No – no!

*The **Monster** stumbles forward – and falls over the body of **Clerval** lying in his way. He recovers and kneels up, and runs his hands wonderingly over **Clerval**'s face – and then, as wonderingly, over his own. He looks up and around, seeing everything for the first time. Then, with heavy grace, he gets to his feet and moves towards the open door. He stops there – looks back once at **Clerval** – then goes out as **Clerval** stirs and groans.*

Clerval   Frankenstein – where are you –

Clerval pushes himself up and looks around. Seeing the empty bench, he staggers up – finds the trailing wire – looks at the open door.

Clerval   It's gone – it's gone! Frankenstein – in God's name, what have you done?

He runs out. A final flash of lightning fills the window. The thunder crashes out and dies away as darkness falls.

Act Two

Inside a simple cottage in the forest. A rough table, a couple of rough chairs, a simple fireplace, a window overlooking some trees. It is neat and clean, but very simply furnished. On the table, the remains of a meal – some bread, an apple, a piece of cheese. Sunlight is streaming in through the window, and through the door upstage, through which we see more trees. To one side there is another door. Birds can be heard singing.

In the distance, there is the furious barking of dogs – like hounds in a hunt. It lasts for a short while and then dies away.

Suddenly the light is blocked in the doorway. The **Monster** is standing there, panting. It is hard to tell what his expression is, though anger and fear seem to mingle in it. He is wearing a torn white shirt which is too small for him, and his hands and arms are torn and bloody.

He stands there nervously for a moment, then makes up his mind and steps in, looking around as if for any threat.

Then he sees the food on the table and seizes it, devouring it ravenously, cramming the bread and cheese into his mouth and sniffing at the apple. His feet are clearly badly torn.

Hearing something, the **Monster** freezes. It is a young man's voice, and a young girl's. During their exchange the **Monster** looks around desperately – sees the other door – makes for it – and gets through, shutting it behind him, just before **Felix** and **Agathe** enter.

Felix	*(Outside)* Not far now. Mind that stone.
Agathe	*(Outside)* Heavens above, Felix, I know there's a stone there. I know every inch of this path . . .
Felix	You ought to carry a stick. I don't know why you don't.
Agathe	What, and go tap-tapping everywhere? I need my hands to carry things in. I'm more agile than you are. And I bet I could find my way back to the cottage from anywhere in these woods, I know them so well . . .

> *They appear in the doorway, just as the* **Monster** *closes the other door.*
> *They are young and simply dressed.* **Felix** *is carrying a musket and a dead rabbit,* **Agathe** *a basket of mushrooms. Although blind, she knows her surroundings so well that she moves around with great freedom.*
> **Felix** *stands the musket in the corner –*

Felix	There. I'll clean that this evening. Time I made some more bullets . . .

> *– and puts the rabbit on the table, but carelessly: he does not notice that the food has been eaten.* **Agathe** *puts her basket there too, and then sits down.*

Agathe	And I'll skin the rabbit in a minute. Shall I make a pie? Or would you like stew?
Felix	He's an old one – he'll be a bit tough. We'll have a stew, and put some of that wild garlic in.
Agathe	And the mushrooms and a carrot or two . . . we're living quite well. Who'd have thought we could?
Felix	Not the judges who sent us here, that's for sure. They thought exile would kill us, as it killed father.
Agathe	We'll survive. We'll do more than survive – we'll prosper.

Felix	We haven't faced winter yet. That won't be so easy . . . look, I think I'll load the gun before I go. Just in case.
Agathe	If you must. But don't expect me to shoot anyone.

*During the discussion **Felix** loads his musket with powder and shot, while **Agathe** fetches and tunes a guitar from the corner of the room.*

Felix	I don't like leaving you alone without any protection. Just point it roughly in the right direction and pull the trigger – that's all you have to do.
Agathe	I don't like the noise.
Felix	All right, swing it round and hit 'em with it, I don't care. But I'll feel better if you have something to protect you, even if you're so brave and independent that you don't want it.

***Felix** uses the musket's ramrod to check that the bullet is firmly in place.*

Agathe	Who's going to attack me, Felix?
Felix	That's a silly question. This is a wild part of the country, Agathe – there are wolves and bears in the forest, even if the bandits are having a day off. And there's been some kind of trouble down in the town. Didn't you hear the dogs earlier on?
Agathe	I thought the men were hunting . . .
Felix	The town dogs were barking too. You must have heard them.
Agathe	Well, if it's down in the town, you'll need the musket more than I will. Oh, I'm not arguing – I know you're right. But I feel safe here.
Felix	No harm in being prepared. If we didn't need more powder and lead I'd leave the rest of the stuff for a day or so, but I might as well get it all . . . what else was it? Flour?
Agathe	And soap, and salt. And if you can find some honey . . .

Felix	We could set up a hive or two ourselves next year. I wonder if I can find anyone who could let me have a queen bee?
Agathe	We'll be living like kings!
Felix	I suppose we could settle here . . . the people in the town are friendly enough, and I could get some kind of work on a farm, perhaps. But it's very lonely for you.
Agathe	Better than prison. Have you loaded that thing yet?
Felix	Just about. It's here in the corner. Remember, you pull back the hammer two clicks. And hold it tight, or you'll hurt yourself.

He stands the gun in the corner and shoulders a canvas bag.

Felix	I'll be back before sundown. D'you want some wood for the fire before I go?
Agathe	No, I'll do that. You go.

He kisses her.

Felix	I should get that rabbit cooking soon, or it'll be like eating a boot.
Agathe	Oh, stop fussing!

Laughing, he goes out.
She puts the guitar down and reaches on to the table for the apple. Feeling that it is not there, she frowns.

Agathe	Oh, you might have left me the apple . . . that's a mean trick.

Her hand finds the loaf, torn and half-eaten. She picks it up to feel it properly.

That's odd . . . it was a fresh loaf.

She feels around for the cheese.

Agathe	And where's the cheese? He hasn't taken that too? Felix, you greedy pig.

She gets up and goes to the door as if to call him back, but changes her mind.

Well, he's got a long way to go, and a lot to carry. But it's not like him to take it without saying anything . . .

She comes back and sits down, picking up the guitar.

Agathe	Anyway, I'm not hungry.

She plucks a chord – then stops abruptly.

Supposing it wasn't Felix, though? . . .

Head alert, listening, she 'looks' around.

Hello? Is anyone there?

Silence.

The door was open . . . anyone could have come in . . . no, I'm being silly. This place is safe.

She begins to play a simple, folk tune.
A few bars into it, the Monster silently appears. He merely stands and listens, as if he has never heard music before.
She comes to the end of her short piece and puts the guitar down, sighing.

No . . . that's too sad. Oh, Papa . . .

She gets up and wanders towards the Monster, who does not move, though he watches her carefully. Beside him on the wall is a picture: the portrait of an elderly man. She comes close and seems to be staring at it. The Monster is holding his breath, as if he is afraid of being discovered — and then he seems to realise that

the girl cannot see him, and moves his hand slowly in front of her face, getting no reaction. A light dawns in his expression, but he does not move.
Then she reaches up, takes the picture from the wall, and goes back to sit down. He stays where he is and listens.

Agathe   Father, I expect it's silly talking to a picture I can't see – it's silly talking to a picture anyway. But I can't worry Felix, and I can't write a diary, and . . . I'm just worried, Papa. Will we survive here? Will we manage to find enough food? Will Felix find work somewhere? – You're silent. You don't know any more than I do. Are you watching over us, Papa? I'm sure you would if you could. But we haven't done badly, have we? We never had to lift a finger before. The servants did it all for us. But we've lived here for six months now, and every so often Felix shoots a rabbit or a couple of pigeons, and there's the apple tree, and I know where the wild strawberries grow . . . I think you *are* looking after us, Papa. You wouldn't leave us on our own . . .

*During this speech the **Monster** silently moves towards the door and goes out.*
She presses the picture to her heart, bowing her head over it.

But it's very hard . . . I wish we'd said goodbye before they took you away. Though I don't know how I could have let you go . . .

*The **Monster** returns. His arms are full of logs. As she sits still with her head bowed, he puts them down very carefully, so as not to make a noise, in the hearth.*
Then he takes an apple from his pocket and puts it on the table – only to freeze and draw his hand back as she looks up at where he is standing. He stands still as she gets up slowly and goes to put the picture back on the wall. Then she picks up a little mirror from the shelf.

Agathe	Thank Heaven, I remember what you looked like, Papa . . . I can judge a real face with my hands now, but I can't judge the expression of a picture. And I can't see my own face any more . . . I used to be pretty. I *think* I was pretty. What I am now, only Felix knows . . .

*She looks in the mirror. The **Monster**, who has come up silently beside her, watches curiously, comparing her face with the image.*
Then she puts the mirror back.

Agathe	It's no good. Everything's changed; there's no point in looking back.

She goes to the fireplace and tries to pick up the basket of logs – but finds it full, and feels them, surprised.

Oh! Felix, you've done it after all! But it's not like you to play tricks on me. Or – I wonder – the bread, the apple – *was it Felix?*

She gets up swiftly and goes to stand in the doorway, as if she is nervous about remaining inside. She looks out, biting a nail.
*Meanwhile the **Monster**, unable to resist it, picks up the mirror, feeling his own face, and slowly brings the glass up and looks in it.*

Monster	Uggghhhh!

*He drops the mirror, which shatters. **Agathe** hears, and turns at once in fear.*

Agathe	Who's that? Who's there?

He leaps to her and seizes her hand before she can run away.

Agathe	(Screams)

He puts his hand over her mouth. She struggles, but he is too strong.

Monster	No! No! Friend!

With one hand he holds her, and with the other he reaches to the table and picks up the apple, which he puts into her hands. As she feels it he says again –

Monster　　Friend! Friend!

Agathe　　You're giving me an apple – who are you? What do you want?

Seeing her relax a little, he releases her. She steps away at once, still fearful.

Monster　　I have come . . . a long way . . . help. Help me.

Agathe　　It was you that ate the bread – and brought the logs in?

Monster　　I will not hurt anyone. I am their friend. Friend of everyone. I give you . . .

He reaches for her hands and folds them around the apple again.

Not hurt anyone. Not kill, not hurt. Friend.

She releases her hands gently and puts the apple on the table.

Agathe　　Let me . . . please, I'm blind, you see . . . may I feel your face? So I can tell what you look like?

Monster　　You see with hands?

Agathe　　It's the only way I can.

Monster　　No. Not touch me. No.

He backs away as she reaches for him.

Agathe　　But you can see what I look like.

He shakes his head, turning away, as her hands reach up to his face.

Monster	No – not good, not good –

Her hands are on his cheeks, his eyes, his mouth. Suddenly she pulls them away and steps back.

Agathe	I'm sorry . . .
Monster	I said *not good.*
Agathe	You poor man!

He is puzzled.

Monster	Man?
Agathe	You must have suffered . . . What's your name?
Monster	No name. Please – you listen. I come a long way. I look for friends. I have no home. Men see me, they hurt me – dogs – they shout, they throw stones. But I am *good*. I want to love them, not hurt, not kill. I come here – I see house – I was hungry, I take food. Pardon. Forgive me. Everywhere I go, they hate me. Am I not good? I look bad. But I am good, I want to help and love – I help you? Bring you food, bring you wood? Please! My heart is unhappy – I stay here? You tell the man?
Felix	*(Calling)* Agathe – are you there?
Agathe	*(Calling)* Felix! Oh, Felix, listen to me –

Felix runs in, sees the Monster apparently attacking her and Agathe apparently struggling to be free, and without hesitation seizes the musket.

Felix	Dear God! He's here –
Agathe	No, Felix! Don't! Don't shoot –
Monster	Tell him!

Agathe	Don't, Felix!
Felix	Out of the way – Agathe, get *down* –
	*But she turns to the **Monster** and clings to him, trying to shield him.*
Agathe	Felix, *listen* –
	*The **Monster**, far stronger than she is, pushes her aside, and as she falls **Felix** shoots. The roar of the musket fills the stage – the **Monster** staggers and cries out –*
Monster	AAAAGGGGGHHHHHHH!
	– and clutching his breast, he staggers to the door, where he clings to the frame.
Agathe	Felix! What have you done?
Felix	Are you hurt? What's he done to you?
	*He runs to **Agathe** and helps her to sit up – but she pushes him away and feels for the **Monster**.*
Agathe	Oh, where are you? Where have you gone?
Felix	Agathe! What are you doing? For God's sake, keep away from him –
	*She reaches the **Monster** and seizes his hand, but he thrusts her away.*
Monster	You *want* me bad! All of you – everyone – you all *want* me bad!
Agathe	No – no –
	***Felix** runs to hold her and keep her back from the **Monster**, who pulls himself up and looks at them both with a face twisted with hatred.*

Monster	Evil? Evil – you *want* evil – then I shall be evil! I shall be terror and hatred and revenge – *revenge!*

With a mighty howl of anger, he runs off.

Agathe	Oh, Felix! What have you done?
Felix	You didn't see him, Agathe – and you don't know what he's done already! The villagers have been hunting him for days –
Agathe	*We* should have understood him, Felix. He was an outcast just like us. We could have helped him – he begged for it! What have you done to him now? Have you made him evil for ever?

She pulls herself away from him and runs out.
Felix makes as if to follow, but stops and sits down in baffled defeat. A long way off we hear:

Monster	*(Howling faintly)* Revenge! Revenge!

Act Three
....

*Frankenstein's study in Geneva. The shape is
the same as that of the room in Act One. There
is no bench nor shelves of medical
specimens; otherwise it is much the same.
Frankenstein is sitting at his desk, his head
resting on his arms.
The shutters are closed, and the room is lit by a
lamp and by the flickering firelight.
After a moment or two, the door opens and
Elizabeth comes in.
Frankenstein looks up.*

Frankenstein	Any news of William?
Elizabeth	No. One of the village girls saw him playing by the lake at four o'clock – she heard the clock chime, so she knew what time it was. He was on his own, under the trees. But, Victor, he's played there dozens of times! It's perfectly safe!
Frankenstein	I know, I know . . . he can't have gone far. I expect he'll turn up soon – he's bound to.

*He gets up and opens the shutter to look out.
It is dark outside.
Elizabeth sinks anxiously into a chair.*

Elizabeth	Oh, what can have happened? Something's wrong, I know it, Victor! Did I tell you about my dreams?
Frankenstein	*(Still at the window)* Those dreams again?
Elizabeth	I can't get them out of my head. There's a monstrous figure – I can't see him clearly, but when he appears, there's such a sense of doom and horror that I wake up crying with fear – what can it mean, Victor?
Frankenstein	It means you need some laudanum to help you sleep. I'll give you some later.
Elizabeth	You don't think I'm going to sleep till they find William, do you?
Frankenstein	No. No, of course not . . . wait. There's someone down there. There's a group of them . . .

Elizabeth jumps up and runs to the window.

Elizabeth   It's the priest ... What's he carrying? Oh, no – it can't be –

*She clings to **Frankenstein**.*

It's William – he's *dead* –

With a desperate cry, she runs from the room.
***Frankenstein** sinks to his knees in despair.*

Frankenstein   *(Groans)* Oh, dear God, this is my doing! I know who did this – why did I ever start this cursed thing?

Suddenly the window is flung open.
*Crouched on the sill, wearing a long, black cloak, his eyes blazing, is the **Monster**.*

Monster   Frankenstein!

Frankenstein   Demon –

*He springs at the **Monster** as if to kill him, but the **Monster** leaps lightly into the room and easily brushes him aside. **Frankenstein** falls, but jumps up again and grapples with him.*

Frankenstein   Murderer! You did this, didn't you? You killed my brother! Monster! Vile thing –

Monster   I am exactly what you made me, Frankenstein.

They struggle together. There is a cry outside and the door handle turns.
*The **Monster** lets **Frankenstein** go, sweeps the hood of the cloak up to cover his face, and sits down with his back to the door. **Frankenstein** staggers away and opens the door.*
***Elizabeth** is there. She clings to **Frankenstein**, weeping. He has to let her come in. She does not see the **Monster**.*

Elizabeth	Strangled! He was killed, Victor – strangled – they found his little body down by the shore –
Frankenstein	Oh, no – no –
Elizabeth	What did he ever do to deserve that? He was the kindest little child – the sweetest little boy – he never hurt a . . . oh, Victor, it's too cruel! I can't bear it . . .

She sobs in his arms. He stands stiffly, conscious all the time of the Monster.

Oh, Victor, come down – you must come and help me – I can't manage on my own – please, Victor, I need you –

She stops suddenly. She has seen the Monster. A moment's petrified silence. Then –

Elizabeth	*(Screams)* Oh, Victor – what – who –
Frankenstein	Leave us, Elizabeth. I must talk to – my visitor. I'll come down in –
Elizabeth	But who is it? Oh, dear God, Victor, what are you doing? What have you done? Oh, am I going mad? I can't bear it –
Frankenstein	I'll explain everything, Elizabeth. But not now. I must talk to this gentleman. Believe me, it's desperately important.
Elizabeth	Victor, your little brother has been murdered! He's lying downstairs! Oh, can't I make you understand?

She runs to the Monster and places a hand on his shoulder.

Please, sir – you must make my cousin help me – tell him to come down with me and –

The Monster turns to look at her. His hood falls back: she sees his face.

Frankenstein	No!
Elizabeth	*(Screams)* The dream! The figure in the dream – Oh, God, help me –

She runs out. **Frankenstein** *moves helplessly as if to follow, but the* **Monster** *is on his feet, holding him back.*

Monster   Let her go. You must listen to me now and do as I say. The time for regrets is past.

Frankenstein   Monster! I didn't create you to do evil – why have you betrayed me?

Monster   I – betray you? If I knew how to laugh, Frankenstein, I'd shake the house with scorn. *You* are the betrayer – you created me, and you made sure I could never be happy. Isn't that betrayal?

Frankenstein   No! I swear it wasn't like that. I made you, yes –

Monster   And as soon as you saw what you'd done, you turned away in horror and left me to find my own way through the world – a creature everyone turned from with disgust and loathing – a vision from a nightmare! But do you know the cruellest thing of all? It was that I wanted to love. I came to life full of goodwill and friendship for every living creature – I wanted to help them and protect them and give them all the love I felt for them – and when I tried, they stoned me and shot at me and set their dogs on me – and even the dogs turned away in disgust . . . Frankenstein, has any man in history ever been more cruel than you have been to me?

Frankenstein   You killed my little brother! Is that love? Is that goodwill?

Monster   Listen! And I'll tell you everything.

He releases **Frankenstein**, *who falls into the chair. The* **Monster** *walks up and down as he speaks;* **Frankenstein** *hides his head in his hands, occasionally looking up to reply – the very picture of despair.*

Monster   When I came to life I knew nothing. I didn't know who I was, I didn't know what the world was – things had no names. The only thing I knew was pain, but I didn't know what that was till much later, when I found out what it was called. Everything was new, Frankenstein. Do you know how beautiful things are when they're new? Or have you forgotten?

Frankenstein   Get on . . .

Monster   Ah, yes. I went down into the town, and they called out their dogs. Creatures full of beauty, with soft fur and bright eyes – I wanted to kneel down and pet them and play with them, but they tore at me with their teeth, and then I knew fear for the first time. I ran to the forest, where it was quiet, where there was cool water to bathe my flesh. The moon came up – oh, Frankenstein, to see the moon for the first time! And I found out what sadness was, and loneliness. Those other beings like myself – they stood upright, like me – they'd thrown stones and shouted harsh words at me, but they had companions, fellows, friends. Couldn't I find a friend? So I began to look . . .

Frankenstein   Where? Where did you look? And how did you learn to speak?

Monster   By listening. By hiding, and listening, and practising by myself. I found a cottage in the forest where a girl and her brother were living – a blind girl, the only piece of luck I ever had. She couldn't see me. We spoke together; oh, I would have been her slave, I would have helped them and worked for them, I would have done anything if they'd only accepted me – but her brother shot me with his musket as if I were a wild beast. It broke my arm. The bullet's still in my shoulder. That was when I found out what pain was really like. All alone in the icy mountains, weeping, crying with rage and loneliness – Frankenstein, you can't imagine how I suffered. If you could imagine it, you'd be on your knees praying to your God for forgiveness.

Frankenstein   *My* God?

Monster   Your God has nothing to do with me. You are my God. You made me, and you owe me happiness. Listen, and I'll tell you the last part of my story. When my wound healed, the bitterness and hatred ebbed away a little; I was still ready to love, still ready to trust . . . you see what you'd made, Frankenstein? A creature better than yourself, perhaps? A nature more noble? Who knows what might have happened if . . . well, I was more cunning by then. More cautious. I thought – it's only grown men and women who hate me; they've learned to be suspicious and to think the worst of people. But if I could find a child, a little innocent creature with no hatred in its heart, then I could take it with me to the wilderness and bring it up as my companion – and we should love each other and live in peace and goodwill with all living creatures –

Frankenstein	No! No – not my brother –
Monster	Be silent.

> *At this point either in the darkness at the back of the stage, or from a trapdoor in the centre of it, a child silently appears. He is dressed in white, with a white expressionless mask, playing silently: the **Ghost of William**. **Frankenstein** sees, and starts up, but the **Monster** holds him back. **Frankenstein** watches in horror as the **Monster** acts out with the child what he is describing, the child also miming.*

I found such a child – a creature like an angel, playing on his own beside the lake. I took his arm – oh, gently, Frankenstein, I had no wish to hurt him. I said, "Come with me, little one" – and he looked at me, and he screamed – I said, "No, hush, I shan't hurt you, but you must come with me" – and he said I shall tell my brother, Herr Frankenstein! He'll punish you, ugly monster!

Frankenstein	Oh, no – no –
Monster	I put my hands to his mouth to silence him, because I was afraid. And your name resounded through my head. You, the creator of my misery. You, the source of all my unhappiness. Frankenstein, a name to curse for ever! And in that moment I thought – Frankenstein is my enemy, and I can hurt him. I can destroy what is his. I can make him as unhappy as he has made me – and I killed your brother, and I laughed! Yes! The one time I have ever laughed. And now you must do something for me.
Frankenstein	Never! I shall destroy you –

> *He leaps at the **Monster**, who easily pushes him away. **Frankenstein** falls to the floor.*

Monster	Not yet. Did you create me to be evil?
Frankenstein	No!
Monster	Did you intend me to be cursed and hated by all mankind?

Frankenstein	No, never –
Monster	Did you create me to be good – to be like human beings but stronger, nobler, kinder – to be an image of what humanity might be?
Frankenstein	Yes, I did. I intended all that. But –
Monster	Then finish what you have started! How can I be good alone? How can I love, when I'm met with nothing but hatred and disgust? Give me a creature like myself, Frankenstein! Give me a mate – a wife – a friend, and we shall leave you alone for ever. We'll go far away from this country, we'll leave Europe altogether, we'll live in the desert or in the cold wilderness of the north – we can survive there where humans can't. But I must have a companion! Foxes – bears – wolves have their mates; every bird has its partner; even rats and mice have their nests, their homes, their families . . . am I to be the only creature in the universe doomed to live alone? Frankenstein, that would be too cruel. Let me be the kind of creature you want me to be – loving, peaceful, harmless, gentle. Let me have someone to love – someone like myself. Make me a companion – make me a wife!

*Pause. **Frankenstein** gets up, walks to window and leans his head on the wall, as if in anguished thought. Then –*

Frankenstein	You swear you'll go then, and not come back?
Monster	I swear it!
Frankenstein	God forgive me . . . I'll do it. It was wrong of me to start; but it would be worse not to finish . . . You can argue well, Monster.
Monster	At last! At last I can hope for something . . . how long?
Frankenstein	Two years.
Monster	Two years!

Frankenstein	I'll have to start from the beginning again, you realise. At least this time I won't have to rely on lightning . . . I've got an electrical machine that's much more powerful than the old one. But I can't hurry the task. Do you want it done properly?
Monster	Of course. Of course, yes, take your time. I can wait. But in two years' time, I shall return.
Frankenstein	In two years' time, it will be ready. But if I hear of you before then, I shall destroy it, and that will be the end.
Monster	You'll hear nothing. I'll be out of sight, but I'll be watching.

He opens the window and springs on to the sill.

Two years, Frankenstein!

He leaps away.

***Frankenstein** sinks to the chair.*

Frankenstein	What have I done? – And yet he was right, I must do it . . .

*A knock at the door, and **Clerval** enters, wearing a heavy overcoat.*

Clerval	Frankenstein – I've just heard the news about your brother – my poor fellow! They're hunting the murderer with dogs. They'll find him, never fear.
Frankenstein	It's too late, Clerval. They won't find him . . . out there.
Clerval	You think not? – But listen, my friend, you must come down. Elizabeth needs you. There are things to be done . . .

***Frankenstein** gets up wearily.*

Frankenstein	Yes. You're right. Oh, Clerval, is there a curse on my family?
Clerval	A curse? No, no. Only bitter misfortune.

Frankenstein leaves. Clerval goes to follow him – sees the open window – goes to close it – looks out. He seems to be seeing the Monster disappearing in the distance, because he starts with surprise, looks at the door, makes as if to call after Frankenstein, then changes his mind and shakes his head.

Clerval   No – it's a trick of the light. It's not possible. But I could have sworn ... *(Calling)* Frankenstein! I'll come with you!

With a last worried look around, he goes out. Darkness falls.

Act Four

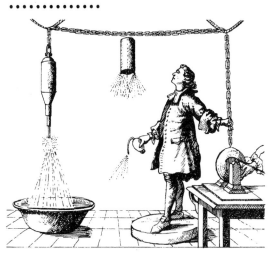

*The same room, two years later. The main difference lies in the fact that there is a bench with a form on it covered by a sheet – the **Monster's Bride** – and, connected to it by all manner of complex wires and clips, a large electrical machine – similar to the small one we saw in Act One, but as tall as a man, and equipped with brass terminals.*
*The shutters are closed; the light is dim. After a moment we hear a key turning in the lock, and then the door opens, and in come **Elizabeth** and **Clerval**. She is carrying a lamp.*
He shuts the door carefully, after listening to make sure that no-one is coming.
She puts the lamp down on the table.

Elizabeth   We haven't got long – he'll be back in an hour or so. I feel like a traitor, like a spy . . .

Clerval   Don't. I'm as suspicious as you are, and I think I know . . .

He sees the sheeted form on the bench, which she still has not noticed. He helps her to sit down with her back to it.

I'm pretty sure I know what he's doing.

Elizabeth   But to keep the room locked for two years! And forbid anyone to come in! It's like Bluebeard's castle . . . Is he mad, Henri? He hasn't been the same since before William was killed. Since he went away to University, in fact.

Clerval   No, I don't think he's mad, Elizabeth. Not mad in the sense of incapable, anyway. He's a genius. He's the greatest man of science the world has ever seen . . .

Elizabeth   If you tell me that, then I believe you. But why is he so unhappy? He's like someone haunted by a demon. Surely a great genius should be happy with the work he's doing?

Clerval   Not if that work is like his.

Elizabeth	But what's he doing? What's he got in here? Why won't he let anyone in? I've thought of stealing his key and letting myself in dozens of times, but I was too afraid of what I'd find – and yet I couldn't imagine what it could be . . . Thank Heaven you came back from Ingolstadt, Henri.
Clerval	I think I know what he's doing. I only hope I can prevent him from doing it again. And I think I know who killed little William. Elizabeth, you must be brave.
Elizabeth	What do you mean? Surely not that Victor himself – but that's not possible! What is he doing?

She looks around wildly and sees the bench. She stands up suddenly.

What's that?

| Clerval | Don't look! I suspected this. Elizabeth, you mustn't touch it – |

He holds her back from going to look at it.

Elizabeth	Then tell me! Tell me what's going on, I beg you!
Clerval	Victor is creating life.
Elizabeth	Creating . . . I don't understand. Creating life? Now I think *I'm* going mad – what is that under there?
Clerval	Listen. When you came to his rooms in Ingolstadt, he'd just finished showing me an experiment – a horrible thing – with a hand – a human hand, taken from a dead body. He could animate it by passing electricity along the nerves. And more than that – he'd put together a complete creature – an artificial man. Do you remember the storm that night?
Elizabeth	I've never heard such thunder – oh, Henri, this is appalling – he'd made a – a –
Clerval	A man, a being, and by attaching a wire to the roof he conducted electricity down from the lightning and . . . brought it to life. He didn't want me to see – at least, he was proud of what he'd done, and

wanted to show someone; but when it came to life I think he was as shocked as I was.

Elizabeth And it did come to life?

Clerval Oh, yes. And this is something I've never told anyone: I saw it on the afternoon William was killed. From this window – down by the lake, among the trees, just as night was falling – a monstrous figure leaping away into the darkness.

Elizabeth looks at the bench.

Elizabeth His visitor . . . The man I saw in his room!

Clerval And *that* looks like another one.

Elizabeth Oh, this is horrible!

She clings to him.

Clerval Elizabeth, you must go downstairs. I'm going to destroy this thing. If he comes back while I'm here, you must keep him away.

Elizabeth Yes – yes. He mustn't finish it. Oh, this is a nightmare . . .

He opens the door for her.

Clerval Remember – do all you can to keep him downstairs while I . . . finish this.

Elizabeth Yes. But what'll he do when he finds out?

Clerval Then we'll have to talk to him. There must be some other way for him to use his gifts . . .

She goes out. He shuts the door and turns back to the bench, preparing himself for what lies under the sheet. He goes to the bench – takes the corner of the sheet as if to fling it aside – then hesitates, and looks around for something. Then he spots it: a large knife, like a cook's knife. He holds it up, testing the blade, and is about to pull the sheet aside when *suddenly the shutters fly open with a crash. In the window, gigantic, enveloped in his cloak, is the figure of the **Monster**.*

Monster   Don't touch her!

*Clerval staggers back with shock, and the **Monster** leaps down into the room.*

Has he sent you to do this?

Clerval   No! He doesn't know I'm here. It's my idea to destroy this thing, and I'll do it – and if I can, I'll destroy you too!

Monster   And that's humanity for you, in a nutshell. Stand away, man.

*Clerval makes as if to attack him, but the **Monster** easily brushes him aside.*

Monster   He made me too well. I'm disgusting to look at, I smell like the grave – but I'm too quick and too strong for you, man, whoever you are. Where is Frankenstein now?

Clerval   On his way home.

*Another attack. This time **Clerval** falls, and the **Monster** bends down and snatches the knife from him.*

Monster   You'll never beat me like this. Why don't I kill you now? Why don't I snuff your life out like a candle? Shall I tell you? It's because he, cursed though he is, made me better than your God made you. It's because when I see a living thing I revere it – I want to cherish it and love it. When a human sees a living thing, his first impulse is to destroy it.

Clerval   That's not true!

Monster   Try living like me, and you'll soon find out how true it is.

Clerval   And the little boy?

*The **Monster** stands up and looks away.*

Monster	That's the one occasion when I behaved like a human being. As a result, it's the one thing I'm ashamed of.

He goes to the bench and pulls down the sheet to disclose the form of his **Bride**. *She is chalk-white, with coarse black hair like his, dark lips, a red scar zigzagging down her face, as hideous as the* **Monster** *in fact. She is dressed in a long white garment like a shroud. Her eyes are closed: she is not yet alive.*
As the **Monster** *looks at her, he shudders and turns away for a moment; but then he makes himself look back.*

Monster Beautiful . . . not like a human being. But we have our own beauty, she and I. Soon you'll wake up, my bride . . . soon we'll be together . . .

Clerval A female –   *Clerval comes to look, and recoils in horror.*

Monster A companion! Don't worry, *man*. We'll go off into the wilderness together; we'll live in peace and kindness –

Clerval And what'll you do then? *Breed?*

He springs to the electrical machine and tears out a handful of wires before the **Monster** *can stop him.*

I'll never let it happen!

Monster *(Roars with anger)*   *The* **Monster** *leaps on* **Clerval** *and pulls him away from the machine – but* **Clerval** *pulls free and grabs another wire. He is about to tear it loose when the* **Monster** *strikes him down. He falls with a cry –*

Clerval Aaaggghhhh!

– The loose end of the wire is still in his hand. The **Monster** *strikes him again and again, until he is unconscious.*

Monster	Murderer! Destroyer! My bride – you've killed my bride –

*When **Clerval** is still, the **Monster** seizes the wire from his hand and stands in helpless agony, looking at the **Bride** and the loose wires that trail from the machine.*

Monster	You shall live! You *shall* live!

Feverishly he tries to connect the wires up again.

Where do they go? Where do they go? Frankenstein, Frankenstein!

*Suddenly the door bursts open. **Elizabeth** is standing there, together with a **Servant** holding two pistols.*

Elizabeth	There – ahhh! *(A gasp of shock as she sees the **Monster**)*
Servant	In God's name, my lady – what is it?
Elizabeth	He's killed Monsieur de Clerval – shoot! Shoot!

*The **Servant** aims both pistols at the **Monster** and fires. The **Monster** staggers back with a cry –*

Monster	Aaaagggghhhh!

*– while **Elizabeth** runs to the body of **Clerval** and kneels beside him. The **Servant** tries hastily to reload – but the **Monster** recovers himself and leaps on him.*

Servant	No! No –
Monster	All killers – all destroyers – every one of you –

*He strikes the **Servant** down as he did **Clerval**. Pausing only to stare down at **Elizabeth** with feverish hatred, he springs back to the **Bride** and attaches the last wire to her head.*

Monster	My bride – awake! Awake!	
		He starts to turn the handle of the great machine. **Elizabeth** *watches in horror –*
Elizabeth	No! Don't do it –	*– as the terminals begin to spark and an electrical hum fills the air. Faster and faster, the* **Monster** *turns the wheel, groaning with effort. The electrical noise increases, sparks fly, but the* **Bride** *does not move.*
Monster	She's not moving – she's not coming alive – they've destroyed you! – No – wait – another wire –	
		Still turning the wheel with one hand, he reaches down and picks up the last loose wire. He looks with desperate urgency to see where it goes – then lets go of the wheel, which continues to turn of its own accord with the momentum, and bends down to slip his arm under her shoulders. He lifts her up, with the wire in his other hand – brings the wire down to touch her heart – and suddenly she convulses into life with a terrifying cry.
Bride	*(Screams)*	
Elizabeth	Oh no! No!	*She crouches in fear as the* **Monster** *and his* **Bride** *cling together in a desperate embrace, surrounded by sparks and a powerful humming and crackling.*
Monster	*(Howling)* Live! Live!	
Bride	*(Cries out)*	*Suddenly the door is flung open.* **Frankenstein** *stands there, looking around with horror.*
Frankenstein	Clerval! Oh no – Elizabeth!	
Elizabeth	Victor – stop them! Stop them!	

Frankenstein leaps to the machine. The Monster, still holding the Bride, cannot stop him as he pulls out handfuls of wires, scattering sparks everywhere and making the strange light from the machine surge, fade, and flicker.

Monster   No! No – she's mine – she's alive –

– but the Bride suddenly throws her arms up straight, her fingers clutching at the air, and then falls lifeless in his arms.

Frankenstein   Never! She'll never live now! Monster, what have you done?

The Monster looks down at her with horror and then lowers her gently on to the bench.

Monster   What have I done, you say? Nothing – compared to what I'm going to do . . .

Before Frankenstein can stop him, the Monster leaps towards Elizabeth and seizes her by the throat.

Elizabeth   No! Help – Victor –

Frankenstein   Put her down! Don't do it –

Monster   *(Horrible snarls of rage)*

He strangles her and drops her lifeless on the floor, then stands laughing as Frankenstein throws himself to his knees beside her.

Frankenstein   Elizabeth – no – no –

Monster   Well, Frankenstein? Your sufferings have begun. How does it feel?

Frankenstein   Demon! Vile thing – destroyer!

Monster   Yes. Destroyer I shall be. I shall destroy *you*, my creator.

*Frankenstein leaps at him – but he avoids
him, and taunts **Frankenstein** from the
window.*

Monster   You'll follow me, Frankenstein. Wherever I go you'll come
stumbling after me, intent on putting me to death – but you won't
catch me!

*Frankenstein runs at him again – and again
fails to grasp the **Monster**.*

Monster   I'll lead you to the ends of the earth – I'll make you follow me to the
coldest, wildest, emptiest places in the world! I'll see you freeze and
starve and suffer – and I'll laugh as you crawl through the barren
mountains, the deserts, the ice-fields . . .

Frankenstein   I'll find you. However long it takes me, I'll follow you to the ends of
the earth, and when I do, I'll tear you apart!

Monster   It'll take you as long as you live. Frankenstein, your sufferings are
just beginning!

*He leaps through the window and vanishes.
Frankenstein kneels again and takes up the
body of **Elizabeth** in his arms.*

Frankenstein   What have I done? What have I done?

*Bows over her, sobbing, as . . .
The lights go down.*

Epilogue
....

*Enter **Captain Walton** dressed as in the Prologue.*
*During **Walton**'s speech, the lights slowly fade up to the same intense brightness as they reached during Prologue.*

Captain Walton   So that was the story Frankenstein told me. When he came to the end, he fell back exhausted, near to death. I left him in the care of one of my men, and went out on deck to breathe the cold air and think for a while about the incredible things I'd heard. But I hadn't been there for long when there was a cry from below. I ran down to the cabin – and saw the Monster crouching on the window-ledge. I shrank away in fear, but the Monster didn't move – for Frankenstein himself lay dead below him. The effort of telling his story had been too much. The creature looked at me and said 'It's ended, then. It's over.' I said 'And what will you do now?' He looked out at the waste of snow and ice, and said 'I shall go north until I can go no further, and then I'll set fire to my sledge and lie down in the flames till my bones have turned to ash. They tell me that human beings have something called a soul, that lives on after their bodies die. I hope I have no soul. All I want now is oblivion . . .' Then he turned and leapt down on to the ice, and drove his sledge away at a furious pace. A minute later he had vanished in the sunlight and the silence.

For a moment there is bright light – and then darkness falls at once.

Activities

The Frankenstein Story

The first Frankenstein film was made in 1910 and showed the monster lurching around the hills.

The story for this play comes from a novel called **Frankenstein**, written by Mary Shelley in 1818. Many people today are familiar with it through films. The picture below is from one of the most famous versions of the story, made in 1931. In it, Boris Karloff played the Monster.

Sometimes the Monster is referred to as Frankenstein, but, in fact, this is the name of its creator. The Monster has no name.

In this adaptation, Philip Pullman has deliberately tried to present the Monster in a different way.

Talk

Complete these tasks in groups.

1   Before you read this play did you know of the Frankenstein story? If so, what was your impression of Frankenstein and the Monster *before* you read this play?

2   Make a list of all the moments during the play which were particularly tense and exciting. In your group, decide which moment you think would be the most frightening on stage and why.

. . . .

Role Play

In pairs, develop these lines from the play.

Elizabeth   What are you doing, Victor? Why don't you
               answer my letters? You haven't even read them!
               If you want to see your father, you'd better come
               tomorrow.

Frankenstein   Tomorrow, but . . .
               ●

Clerval   It's gone – it's gone! Frankenstein – in God's
               name what have you done here?

Frankenstein   . . . .
               ●

Agathe   You're giving me an apple – who are you? What
               do you want?

Monster   . . . .
               ●

Monster   Let her go. You must listen to me now and do as
               I say. The time for regrets is past.

Frankenstein   Monster, I didn't create you to do evil – why ha
               you betrayed me?

Monster   . . . .
               ●

Improvise

Act 4 ends with Frankenstein sobbing over his dead cousin's body. By the very end of the play Frankenstein and the Monster have reached the Arctic Circle.

In groups, imagine what Frankenstein and the Monster would have been thinking and feeling after Elizabeth's death.

Decide what might have happened next.

Plan where they might have gone and who they might have met.

Think of some likely situations for two travellers – for example, getting food or shelter, meeting other travellers, etc.

Make up two or three scenes in which you present what might have happened on their travels through Europe to the Arctic Circle.

Modern Frankensteins

In the years before Mary Shelley wrote her novel there was great interest in
the power of science. In the play Frankenstein refers to an 'Italian called
Galvani' when he is talking about frogs' legs. In the picture below you can
see one of his experiments in progress. Galvani showed how limbs can
move when electricity is passed through them and gave Shelley the idea for
Frankenstein.

Talk

1   **In groups, study the pictures on the facing page.** Each one shows what
    'modern Frankensteins' can do. For each one decide what is happening
    and what is being created.

2   What other examples of recent scientific discoveries in which scientists
    create something can you think of? List them.

3   Could any of the discoveries that you have discussed, like Frankenstein's
    creation, go wrong? Explain what you mean.

A scientist placing a test tube containing human sperm and ova (eggs) into an incubator where fertilization should occur. The fertilized ovum will then be transferred to the mother's womb.

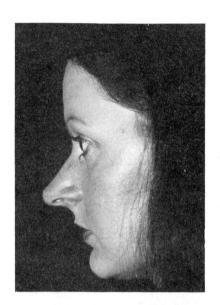

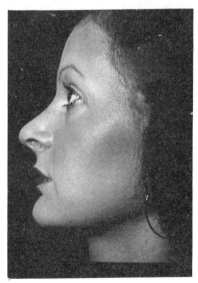

An artifical heart valve to be implanted during open heart surgery. The surgeon will re-start the heart following the replacement of the valve.

Before: (top picture) This woman will undergo cosmetic surgery to reduce the size of her nose.
After: (bottom picture) The operation has been completed.

. . . .

Mime

Frankenstein's machine.

You are going to become this machine in groups of about six! In your group, decide what the main parts of the machine are, for example, wheels, handles, wires etc.

Each person works out his or her own movement as part of the machine and you gradually put all these together. Stay completely still to start with and then gradually build up your own 'electricity'. You could add sound effects to this.

. . . .

Design

From what you have read and done, plan and then draw your own version of a Frankenstein machine.

. . . .

Music

Either make up a piece of music to go with the moments in the play when a monster is brought to life

Or choose which moments would be helped by sound effects and make a sound effects tape to go with the play.

. . . .

Write

Frankenstein tries to create a perfect creature but fails. Write a story in which you explore this idea.

It could be about someone trying to create a monster;

It could be about a doctor introducing a new but dangerous treatment;

It could be about someone who sacrifices everything to achieve something his or her heart is set on.

Outsiders

Talk

In pairs, answer these questions:

1 How do you react to
   a someone with a birthmark or scar

   b someone who has a different colour skin to yours?

2 Have you ever been a member of a gang? If so what did you do if someone you didn't like tried to join the gang?

3 How do you treat someone new to your school or where you live?

4 Why do you think very young children react to disabled people in a different way from some adults?

5 Have you ever judged someone by their appearance and then found out later that you were totally wrong? Be honest and explain fully!

Make a list of anyone you would describe as an outsider or an outcast.

· ·

Think   **What do these lines from the play suggest to you?**

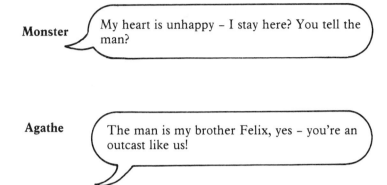

Monster   My heart is unhappy – I stay here? You tell the man?

Agathe   The man is my brother Felix, yes – you're an outcast like us!

· ·

Act   1   Why do you think Agathe and Felix are living apart from the other villagers?
        2   What kind of person is Agathe?
        3   In what ways are she and the Monster similar?

Imagine that Felix does not return for several minutes after the lines you have just been looking at.

Continue this scene in a way that shows how Agathe and the Monster have certain things in common with each other.

Read

The Hunchback in the Park

Dylan Thomas

The hunchback in the park,
A solitary mister
Propped between trees and water
From the opening of the garden lock
That lets the trees and water enter
Until the Sunday sombre bell at dark

Eating bread from a newspaper
Drinking water from the chained cup
That the children filled with gravel
In the fountain basin where I sailed my ship
Slept at night in a dog kennel
But nobody chained him up.

Like the park birds he came early
Like the water he sat down
And Mister they called Hey Mister
The truant boys from the town
Running when he had heard them clearly
On out of sound

Past lake and rockery
Laughing when he shook his paper
Hunchbacked in mockery
Through the loud zoo of the willow groves
Dodging the park keeper
With his stick that picked up leaves.

And the old dog sleeper
Alone between nurses and swans
While the boys among willows
Made the tigers jump out of their eyes
To roar on the rockery stones
And the groves were blue with sailors

Made all day until bell time
A woman figure without fault
Straight as a young elm
Straight and tall from his crooked bones
That she might stand in the night
After the locks and chains

All night in the unmade park
After the railings and shrubberies
The birds the grass the trees the lake
And the wild boys innocent as strawberries
Had followed the hunchback
To his kennel in the dark.

• •

Talk

1   Why do you think the boys from the town made fun of the hunchback?

2   How do you react to people who are physically different from you and avoided by others?

3   Make a list of all you know about what the Monster looked like physically in **Frankenstein.**

4   Who treats the Monster most sympathetically in the play? Why? How would you have treated 'it'?

5   In what ways are the Monster and the hunchback,

    a *similar*   b *different?*

6   How would you know a Monster if you couldn't see its face?!

• •

Write

Make up a poem in which you present things from the Monster's point of view. Look carefully at the lines spoken by the Monster to Frankenstein before you try this.

What the Playwright Said

Read

Study what Philip Pullman says about his adaptation of **Frankenstein**.

Frankenstein is a story about what it means to be human. One of the things that makes us human (perhaps *the* thing) is language, and the Monster's increasing command of language is one of the things which any production needs to bring out.

In the book, the Monster himself tells a lot of the story. He tells how he finds the cottage in the forest, and hides nearby, listening to the family through the wall and learning little by little how to understand them.

In a play, though, it is not possible to show things happening gradually over a long period. You have to find dramatic moments, single incidents which arise from what's gone before and set the course for what will happen next. So in Act 3, the Monster is already able to speak at least as well as Frankenstein. His long speeches are very important, and they should be spoken clearly and passionately and powerfully, as a brilliant lawyer speaks in court. If the actor playing the Monster has gained the audience's sympathy in the previous Acts, they will listen to the speeches with close attention.

Something I wanted to get away from in this play was the lurching, lumpish monster, hands outstretched, that everyone can imitate jokingly. Mary Shelley in the novel stresses the Monster's athleticism and speed, and after all Frankenstein created him to be powerful and active. If the Monster looks as ugly as a corpse, but moves with the grace and energy of a dancer or a gymnast, the effect is electric. Literally!

The final section, with the Monster trying to bring the Bride to life and Frankenstein destroying it, and the other characters dying, must not be taken slowly. The sections must follow each other almost too swiftly for thought, as in a dream, otherwise the tension goes out of it and all the corpses piling up look merely funny.

One major change I made was to have the blind person, whom the Monster tries to befriend, a young woman instead of an old man. In the book, there are three people in the cottage: Felix, Agathe, and their blind father. You might feel that in making this change, I was being sexist, and wanting to exploit the contrast between a powerful male monster and a frail, helpless female. On the other hand, you might feel that I was providing a more interesting role for an actress in a story where women have otherwise very little to do. I know which I think I was doing.

Philip Pullman

Talk

1 How do you think the Monster should talk so that it seems 'human'?
Try out a number of different voices. Try to avoid making it sound funny.

2 What do you feel about Phillip Pullman's introduction of a blind young woman instead of a blind old man?
Do you think this works?

Research

1 Find out about Mary Shelley's life and about other works she wrote.

2 Find out what the word 'gothic' means when applied to literature.

Drama Ideas

1   Frankenstein on Trial

Put the creator of the Monster on trial. You will need a prosecutor and someone to defend him. In threes, act out the questioning of Frankenstein. Present your scene to the class and let them judge whether he is guilty or not.

· ·

2   **Being Blind**

Try these exercises to help you to understand Agathe's point of view.

In pairs:

a   *One person is 'blind' and leads the other person around the room using touch and then speech.*

b   *Describe your partner's face by talking as you touch her/him.*

c   *With a blindfold, try and guess what a number of typical household items are by feeling them.*

d   *Describe an object to your 'blind' partner, without using its name, until s/he guesses what it is.*

e   *Act out part of the scene with Agathe and Felix, trying to play Agathe as realistically as you can.*

3   **The Monster's Revenge**

Monster

How many stories do you know or have you read which involve one person getting their revenge on someone else?

In a group of four to six make up a story in which there is injustice and revenge. Act out your story.

4 A Horror Story

In groups, make a list of the things that you think go to make up a good horror story. For example, strange creatures, scarey settings etc.

Choose up to ten sound effects to go with your story.

Work out the plot of a horror story.

Tell it to the rest of the class, using a mixture of acting, story-telling and sounds to make it as lively and frightening as possible.

Frankenstein on Stage

This version of **Frankenstein** was first performed by Polka Children's Theatre in 1988.

Talk

Decide when each of these photographs was taken and which lines were being spoken at the time.

Designing the Set

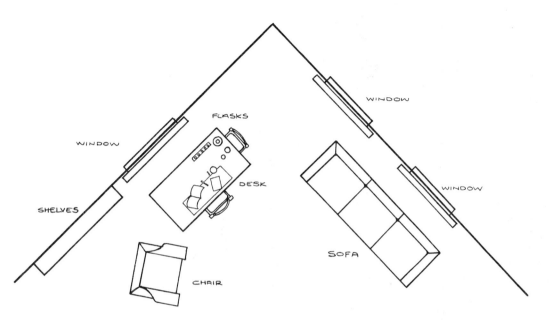

Think

Study this diagram of the set for the opening act of the play. What is missing? Copy and complete it in your own way.

Design

Choose two other acts from **Frankenstein**. Draw set diagrams for them.

Make

Plan, design and then make Frankenstein's electric machine.

When **Frankenstein** was produced at the Polka Children's Theatre, Wimbledon, in 1988, the cast was as follows:

Victor Frankenstein	*Gerry Nowicki*
Henri Clerval	*Thomas Marty*
Elizabeth	*Sarah Huntley*
The Monster	*Peter Gallagher*
Agatha, the Apparition, the Bride	*Hélène Demetriades*
Captain Walton, Felix, a Servant	*Richard Doubleday*

The play was directed by Roman Stefanski.

ACKNOWLEDGEMENTS

'The Hunchback in the Park' by
Dylan Thomas on p. 67 is reprinted
by permission of J.M. Dent & Sons Ltd
on behalf of the Trustees for the Copyrights
of the late Dylan Thomas.

The illustrations are by Jonathon Heap.
The handwriting is by Elitta Fell.

The publishers would like to thank the following
for permission to reproduce photographs:

British Film Institute, p. 59 (both), 76;
Mary Evans Picture Library, p. 24, 62, 70;
Polka Children's Theatre, p. 74 (all);
Science Photo Library, p. 63 (all).

Cover design: Peter Stone

Other plays in this series include:

Across the Barricades   ISBN 0 19 831272 5
    Joan Lingard   adapted by David Ian Neville

The Burston School Strike   ISBN 0 19 8312741
    Roy Nevitt

The Demon Headmaster   ISBN 0 19 831270 9
    Gillian Cross   adapted by Adrian Flynn

Hot Cakes   ISBN 0 19 831273 3
    Adrian Flynn

Paper Tigers   ISBN 0 19 831268 7
    Steve Barlow and Steve Skidmore

A Question of Courage   ISBN 0 19 831271 7
    Marjorie Darke   adapted by Bill Lucas and Brian Keaney

The Teen Commandments   ISBN 0 19 831275 X
    Kelvin Reynolds

Tigers on the Prowl   ISBN 0 19 8312776
    Steve Barlow and Steve Skidmore

The Turbulent Term of Tyke Tiler   ISBN 0 19 831269 5
    adapted from her own novel by Gene Kemp